CONTENTS

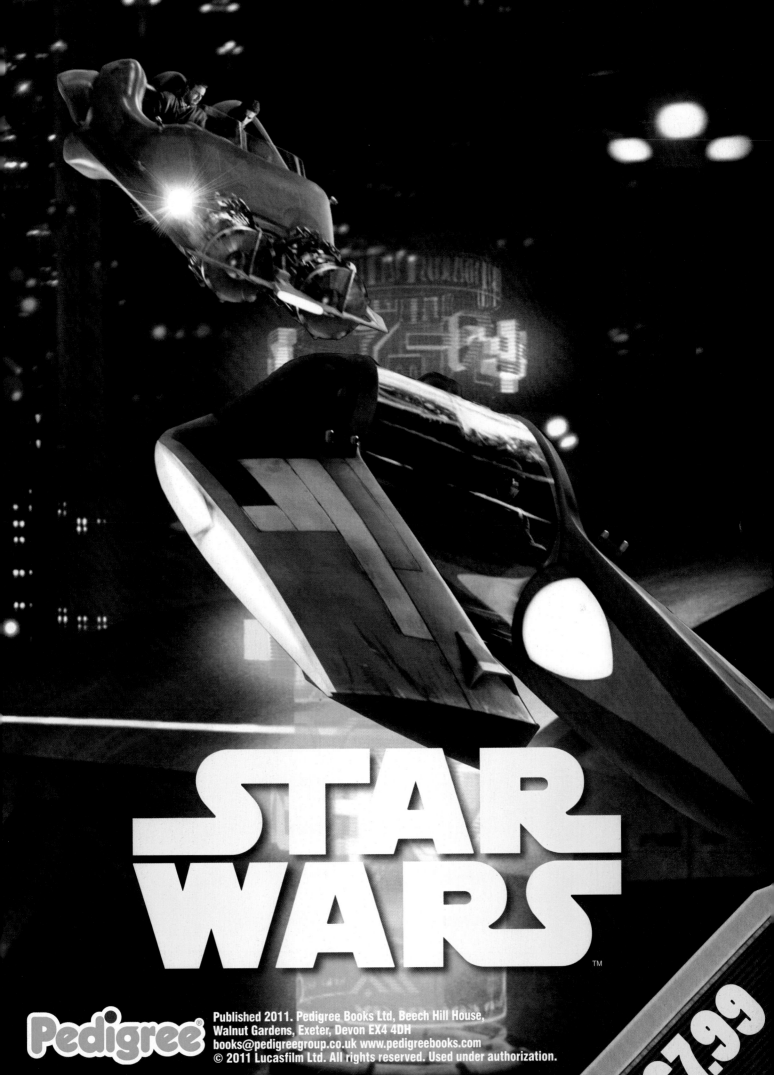

STAR WARS™

Published 2011. Pedigree Books Ltd, Beech Hill House,
Walnut Gardens, Exeter, Devon EX4 4DH
books@pedigreegroup.co.uk www.pedigreebooks.com

Pedigree®

£7.99

INTRODUCTION

Welcome to this special starships and technology edition. Inside you will find fascinating extracts from the Holocron datafiles, as well as guides to help you draw your favourite starships and puzzles to test your knowledge.

Accompany the most famous heroes in the galaxy as they face danger, excitement and adventure. You will discover loyal friends and treacherous enemies.

MAY THE FORCE BE WITH YOU!

The Phantom Menace

T he Galactic Republic was in a state of confusion. The Trade Federation had stopped anyone visiting or leaving the planet of Naboo.

Jedi Master Qui-Gon Jinn and his Padawan, Obi-Wan Kenobi, boarded the Trade Federation ship to try to settle the conflict. However, they were attacked by destroyer droids! As they were battling for their lives, they saw an invasion army of battle droids.

By hiding aboard Trade Federation battleships, the Jedi reached the planet's surface, planning to warn Queen Amidala about the invasion army. A clumsy Gungan called Jar Jar Binks introduced them to his leader, Boss Nass.

Although he wasn't fond of the Naboo people, Boss Nass agreed to lend the Jedi his bongo. They had a perilous journey through the core of the planet, but at last they reached the capital city of Naboo.

The Jedi helped the Queen to escape in her sleek Naboo cruiser, and they set a course for Coruscant to ask for the Republic's help. They were joined by Jar Jar Binks and a droid called R2-D2.

No one guessed that a Sith lord called Darth Sidious was behind the blockade of Naboo. When he heard that the Queen had vanished, he sent his apprentice Darth Maul to find her.

The Naboo cruiser's hyperdrive was leaking, forcing the Jedi to land on Tatooine. A dealer called Watto had the parts they needed, but they had no money – and Qui-Gon's Jedi mind tricks wouldn't work on the Toydarian!

Watto's slave boy, Anakin Skywalker, made friends with Qui-Gon and the Queen's handmaiden, Padmé. He had always dreamed of becoming a pilot, and now he saw a chance to make his dreams come true. He offered to help Qui-Gon by entering a Podrace and letting him use the prize money to buy parts.

Qui-Gon sensed that the Force was unusually strong with Anakin. He felt certain that the boy was very special. But while Anakin was preparing for the race, Darth Maul was arriving on Tatooine. »

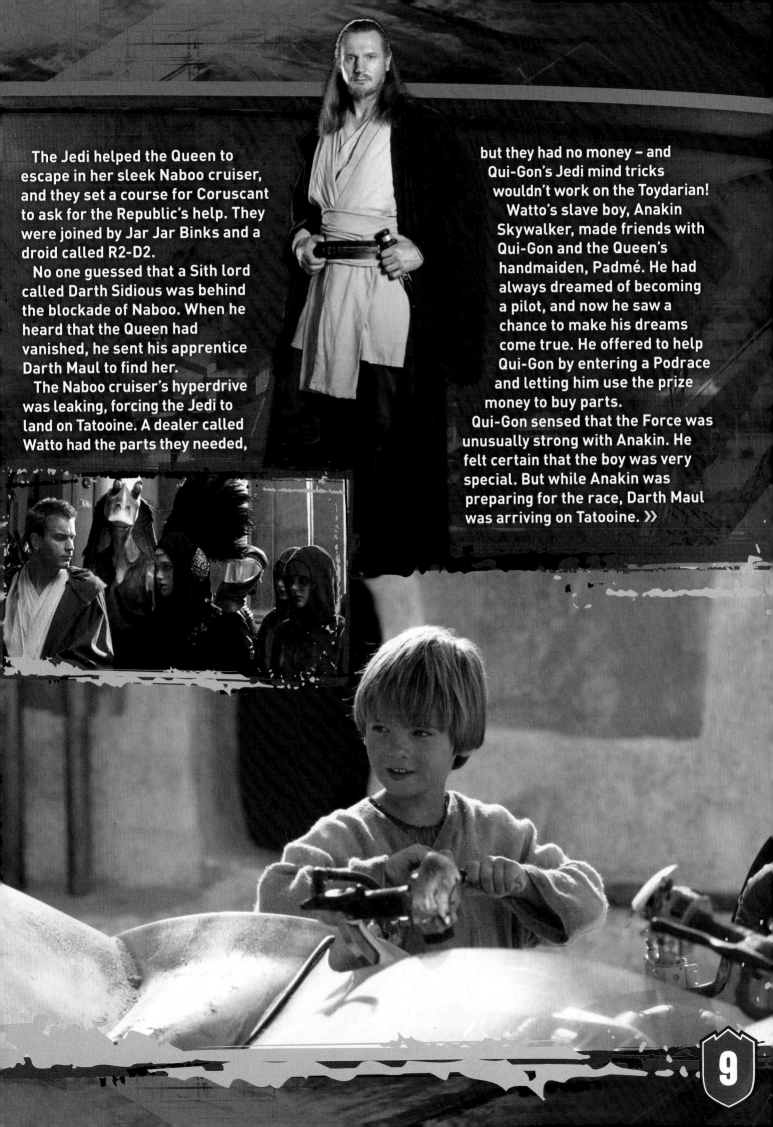

The Phantom Menace

It was an exciting, nail-biting Podrace. Anakin's superior flying skills enabled him to defeat the cheating Sebulba, and to everyone's delight he won the race. Qui-Gon's deal with Watto meant that he could take the parts for his ship and set Anakin free. He planned to take him to Coruscant and train him as a Jedi. Anakin said goodbye to his mother and they prepared to leave.

Suddenly, Darth Maul came hurtling across the sands towards them. He and Qui-Gon began a deadly duel.

Qui-Gon escaped with his life and the furious Darth Maul was left behind on Tatooine. But when the Jedi reached Coruscant, they found the Senate in turmoil.

The Supreme Chancellor had no real power and could not help the Queen to fight the blockade on her planet. She called for a vote of no confidence, and Senator Palpatine was nominated as the new Supreme Chancellor. The Queen decided to return to Naboo to be with her people.

The Jedi Council tested Anakin, but they found that he was too full of fear to become a Jedi. Qui-Gon vowed to train the boy himself. He and Obi-Wan returned to Naboo with the Queen, taking Anakin with them. Secretly, Lord Sidious ordered Darth Maul to follow the Queen to Naboo.

On Naboo, Padmé revealed that she was the true Queen Amidala! She had been using a decoy to fool her enemies. She

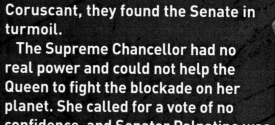

quickly made an alliance with Boss Nass, knowing that she would need the help of the Gungans to defeat the Trade Federation.

The Gungans drew the droid army away from the capital city while Padmé led a strike team into the city to capture the Viceroy. She also sent pilots into space to disable the droid control ship. Anakin hid inside the cockpit of a spare fighter with R2-D2 and watched the pilots taking off, ready to attack the droid control ship.

Suddenly there was a volley of laser fire as destroyer droids rolled into the hangar. At that moment, Darth Maul appeared! He ignited his double-bladed lightsaber and his red eyes glowed with evil.

As the Jedi fought Darth Maul, Anakin turned his fighter on the destroyer droids and shot them down. But his fighter was now on automatic pilot, and it carried him up into space to join the battle!

The Jedi were struggling to defeat Darth Maul. He was a skilled warrior, and at last he drove his lightsaber into Qui-Gon's body. Obi-Wan was a superb duellist and he finally killed the Sith apprentice – but he was too late to save his Master. Obi-Wan promised Qui-Gon that he would train Anakin as a Jedi.

In the skies above the planet, Anakin and R2-D2 flew into the destroyer droids. Anakin shot at the main reactor and escaped as it exploded into tiny pieces. The droid soldiers stopped working!

The Trade Federation had been defeated, but the galaxy was changing. Palpatine was the new Supreme Chancellor and the threat of the Sith was lurking in the shadows. The Jedi could sense dark times ahead. ■

TRUE or FALSE?

Test your technical know-how! Which of these statements are true? Write down 'True' or 'False' beside each statement, and then check the answers page to discover your mark out of ten.

1 The X-wing starfighter holds ten passengers.
TRUE   FALSE

2 Mace Windu's lightsaber had a purple blade.
TRUE   FALSE

3 Han Solo won the Millennium Falcon from Jabba the Hutt.
TRUE   FALSE

4 Boss Nass's Bongo was destroyed by Qui-Gon Jinn.
TRUE   FALSE

5 Boba Fett's turbo jetpack once belonged to his father.
TRUE   FALSE

6 Destroyer droids are hand-held explosive devices.
TRUE   FALSE

7 The Separatist droid army was built on Geonosis.
TRUE   FALSE

8 The Death Star was designed by Bail Organa.
TRUE   FALSE

9 The dart that killed Zam Wesell was made on Tatooine.
TRUE   FALSE

10 The Republic's clone soldiers were grown on Kamino.
TRUE   FALSE

MY SCORE:

SLEIGHT OF HAND

A Jedi Knight needs lightning-fast reflexes. Are your reactions quick enough?
Use this simple card trick to practise your sleight of hand.

1 Hold the deck of cards in your hand.

2 Ask your friend to choose a card and look at it carefully.

3 Here's the tricky bit. While your friend is distracted by concentrating on the card, turn the whole deck over. Then turn over the top card so that it is facing down.

4 Ask your friend to replace his or her card in the deck.

5 Explain that you are going to find the card your friend chose.

6 Put the deck of cards behind your back and turn the top card over. Say that you are using your magic powers to make your friend's card roll over in the pack.

7 Hand over the deck of cards and ask your friend to look for the card he or she chose. Say that you have made it roll over, so it will be the only one facing upwards!

13

Holocron Datafile:
Lightsaber

The elegant lightsaber is the distinctive weapon of a Jedi. Those who carry lightsabers have great skill, unusual dexterity and are strong in the Force. Read and learn about lightsabers, and then use the grid to draw your own version of this classic weapon.

Did You Know?

Darth Maul's double-bladed lightsaber was made from two hilts fused together.

Fact File

An unignited lightsaber looks like a long metal handle. Inside the handle are a power cell and up to three crystals. These crystals focus the energy from the power source, releasing it as a shaft of pure energy. It hums and shimmers, and is able to cut

Lightsaber Parts

- Blade arc tip
- Blade emitter shroud
- Blade energy channel
- Blade length adjust
- Blade power adjust
- Crystal energy chamber
- Cycling field energizers
- Diatium power cell
- Energy gate
- Energy modulation circuits
- Focusing crystal activator
- Focusing crystals
- Inert power insulator
- Magnetic stabilizing ring
- Power field conductor
- Power vortex ring
- Primary crystal with mount
- Ring tuning flange

Did You Know?

Each Jedi makes his or her own lightsaber during training.

HILT STYLES

Adept
Adjudicator
Arbiter
Avenger
Champion
Consul
Defender
Firebrand
Guardian
Praetor
Retaliator
Sentinel
Vanquisher
Vindicator

through almost anything – except another lightsaber.

These deadly weapons require a Jedi to handle them correctly and wisely. However, they are also used by the Sith, who can match the Jedi in skill and strength in the Force. The colour of the blade depends on the crystal. Towards the end of the Republic, most Jedi used blue and green blade-producing crystals from Ilum. The Sith used crystals that produced red blades, and they seemed to prefer their blades to be the colour of blood.

Jedi learn how to use lightsabers at a very young age. They learn duelling techniques as part of their training. For a true Jedi, a lightsaber is more than a weapon. It can help the user to develop a stronger connection with the Force.

Pyramid Puzzle

Solve the clues and rearrange the letters in the shaded squares to find the hidden name of a Rebel hero.

1.

2.

3.

4.

5.

1 Jedi weapon.

2 A small Jedi craft designed for combat.

3 Where does an aquata breather allow the user to breathe?

4 Yoda fled into exile aboard a star-shaped escape ____.

5 A powerful pole-arm wielded by General Grievous.

ODD ONE OUT

A

B

C

D

E

F

G

H

I

J

K

L

Which of these magnificent starships is the odd one out?

COLOUR BY

NUMBERS

Darth Maul has defeated Qui-Gon Jinn – can he also destroy Obi-Wan Kenobi? Use the colour code to complete this exciting duel scene.

1
2
3
4
5
6
7

Attack of the Clones

Ten years had passed since the Trade Federation had blockaded Naboo, and once again there was trouble in the Galactic Senate. An ex-Jedi called Count Dooku had persuaded thousands of solar systems to leave the Republic. These Separatists wanted to bring an end to the Republic. The Jedi were struggling to keep peace and order, and some Senators wanted to create their own army.

Padmé was now a Senator, and she was against the idea of creating an army of the Republic. Because she was so outspoken, there had been an attempt on her life. Obi-Wan and his Padawan Anakin were assigned to protect her.

That night there was another attempt on Padmé's life. The Jedi chased the assassin through the streets of Coruscant in a speeder. At last they caught up with her and began to question her.

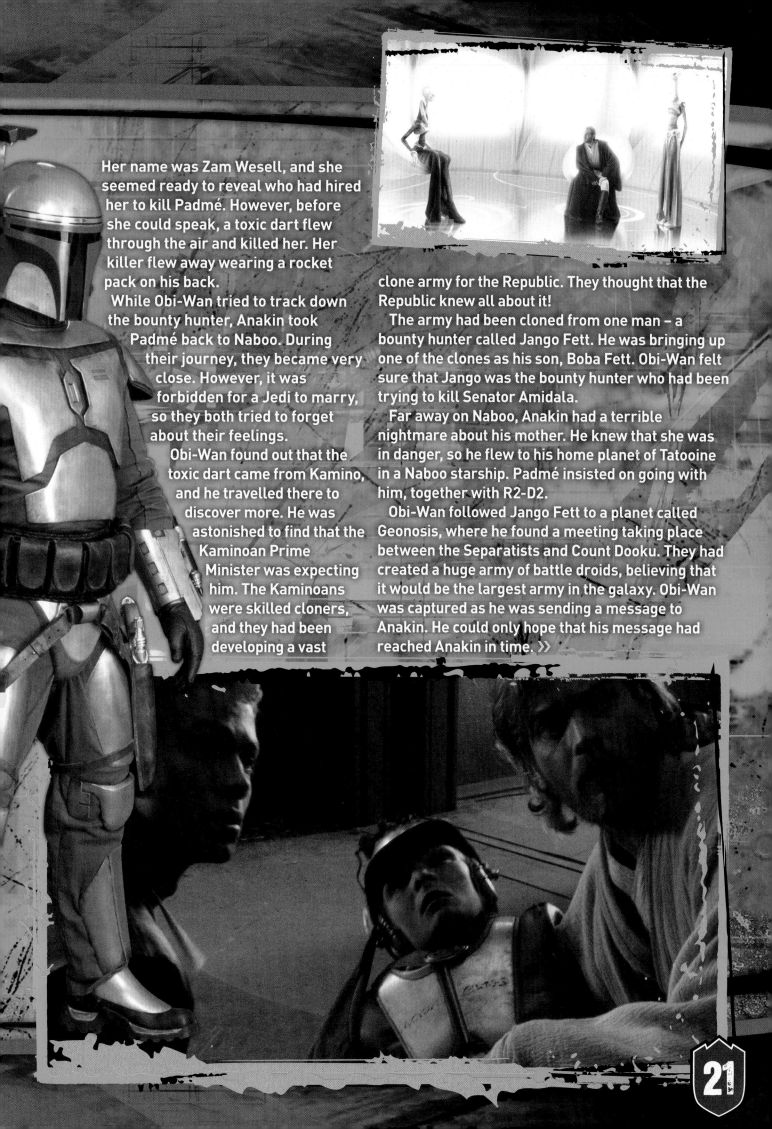

Her name was Zam Wesell, and she seemed ready to reveal who had hired her to kill Padmé. However, before she could speak, a toxic dart flew through the air and killed her. Her killer flew away wearing a rocket pack on his back.

While Obi-Wan tried to track down the bounty hunter, Anakin took Padmé back to Naboo. During their journey, they became very close. However, it was forbidden for a Jedi to marry, so they both tried to forget about their feelings.

Obi-Wan found out that the toxic dart came from Kamino, and he travelled there to discover more. He was astonished to find that the Kaminoan Prime Minister was expecting him. The Kaminoans were skilled cloners, and they had been developing a vast clone army for the Republic. They thought that the Republic knew all about it!

The army had been cloned from one man – a bounty hunter called Jango Fett. He was bringing up one of the clones as his son, Boba Fett. Obi-Wan felt sure that Jango was the bounty hunter who had been trying to kill Senator Amidala.

Far away on Naboo, Anakin had a terrible nightmare about his mother. He knew that she was in danger, so he flew to his home planet of Tatooine in a Naboo starship. Padmé insisted on going with him, together with R2-D2.

Obi-Wan followed Jango Fett to a planet called Geonosis, where he found a meeting taking place between the Separatists and Count Dooku. They had created a huge army of battle droids, believing that it would be the largest army in the galaxy. Obi-Wan was captured as he was sending a message to Anakin. He could only hope that his message had reached Anakin in time. »

Attack of the Clones

On Tatooine, Anakin's mother had been living on a moisture farm with her new husband Cliegg Lars. But she had been captured by cruel Tusken Raiders, and Anakin arrived too late to save her. She died in his arms.

Filled with hatred, Anakin ignited his lightsaber and killed every single Tusken Raider. His anger overpowered every other thought and feeling, and he would never be free of it again.

Anakin and Padmé received Obi-Wan's message and transmitted it to the Jedi Council. Anakin was determined to save his Master. Against orders, they set a course for Geonosis. They took R2-D2 with them, as well as C-3PO, the protocol droid Anakin had built as a boy.

Meanwhile, in the Senate, Supreme Chancellor Palpatine was granted emergency powers so that he could make fast decisions during the Separatist crisis. His first decision was to use the clone army to fight the Separatists.

Almost as soon as Padmé and Anakin arrived on Geonosis, they were captured and condemned to death. As they were led into the execution arena, they declared their love for each other. They were tied up alongside Obi-Wan, and the Separatists eagerly prepared to watch them die.

Three monstrous beasts were released into the arena, and Count Dooku gave a cruel smile. However, his triumph turned to astonishment as the captives defeated the beasts!

Suddenly, all around the arena, dozens of Jedi Knights pulled off their cloaks and ignited their lightsabers. Count Dooku summoned his droid

soldiers and a bloody battle began.

The Jedi fought bravely to protect each other. Mace Windu sent Jango Fett's head flying from his shoulders and there were acts of heroism all around the arena. However, the Jedi were hopelessly outnumbered. It was only a matter of time before they were beaten.

Suddenly, a fleet of gunships descended into the arena. Yoda was there, in command of thousands of clone troopers. The Republic army had arrived!

Count Dooku zoomed away on a speeder, but Anakin and Obi-Wan followed him and engaged him in combat. Dooku knocked Obi-Wan out and cut off Anakin's arm. He turned to leave and found himself facing his old Master – Yoda.

A lightning-fast duel began. Dooku and Yoda were skilled warriors, but Yoda's experience gave him the edge. Dooku could not defeat him. He resorted to cheating, attacking the defenceless Obi-Wan and Anakin. While Yoda was protecting them, Dooku escaped.

The Battle of Geonosis was the first battle of many in the Clone Wars. It had far-reaching consequences. Anakin married Padmé in secret. Supreme Chancellor Palpatine ordered thousands more clone troopers. And all across the galaxy, planets prepared for war. ∎

Holocron Datafile:
X-Wing Starfighter

The X-wing starfighter was famously used by the Rebel Alliance, and is one of the best single-pilot starships ever produced. Read and learn about the X-wing starfighter, and then use the grid to draw your own version of this stylish vessel.

SUMMARY

Size: 12.5 metres long
Type: Starfighter
Weapon: Laser cannons, proton torpedoes
Affiliation: Rebel Alliance
Manufacturer: Incom Corporation
Cargo capacity: 2 cubic metres, 110 kilograms.

Fact File

The Incom Corporation designed and built the X-wing. When the company was nationalised by the Empire, the senior design team joined the Rebellion, bringing along the plans and prototypes for their new starfighter.

Rogue Squadron

X-wing squadrons can be identified by the coloured stripes on the wings. At the Battle of Yavin, Luke Skywalker was part of Red Squadron. His X-wing had five red stripes and was called Red Five. After the battle, he and Wedge Antilles were the only surviving members of Red Squadron. They renamed their X-wing unit Rogue Squadron, and became known throughout the galaxy for their courage and flying talent.

Did You Know?
The starship got its name because of the double-layered wings. They separate into an X shape during combat to increase the pilot's field of fire.

Did You Know?
The X-wing has a blind spot at the rear of its belly.

Each X-wing has four high-powered laser cannons, six proton torpedoes, deflector shields, a hyperdrive engine and an astromech droid, as well as a reinforced titanium alloy hull and transparisteel canopy. Unlike the Imperial TIE fighters, the X-wings can launch and land without special support.

The astromech droid sits in a socket behind the cockpit and acts as a co-pilot and technician. In an emergency, the X-wing can eject the pilot and the astromech unit and throw them clear of the fighter.

An X-wing holds enough oxygen, fuel and power to last a week. When the ship lands, the air supply can be renewed and the water and life-support systems can be recharged. The cargo bay holds survival gear in case the pilot lands in a dangerous or remote place.

SUDOKU

The engineers who design and build the galaxy's starships are gifted logicians. They are talented at understanding numbers and making patterns.

Would you make a good engineer? See how quickly you can solve this complicated Sudoku puzzle.

Fill in all the empty squares so that every row, every column and every 3x3 square contain the numbers 1 to 9.

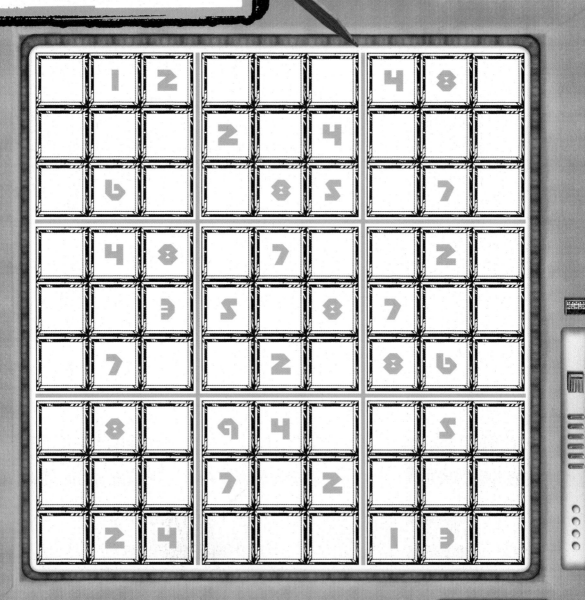

PHOTOFIT

1

2

3

4

5

All sorts of villains and criminals visit the Mos Eisley cantina. Match the names of these dangerous characters to their Wanted posters.

A. GARINDAN

B. GREEDO

C. KABE

D. MUFTAK

E. DR EVAZAN

A GAME FOR UP TO FOUR PLAYERS

10

An enemy starship fires on you. Go back three spaces.

8

7

Secret modifications increase your speed. Go forward one space.

11

12

You have a vision of yourself on Mustafar. Have another turn.

14

28

You evade an enemy starship. Have another turn.

26

25

24

29

30

You waste time investigating a mysterious planet. Miss a turn.

32

46

45

You hear Obi-Wan Kenobi's voice encouraging you. Go forward three spaces.

43

42

Your weapons malfunction. Miss a turn.

47

48

49

50

1 Pick a counter to represent each starship.
2 Choose which vehicle each player will fly.
3 Throw the dice and move the counter along the board.
4 Obey the instructions written on the squares you land on.
5 The winner is the first player to reach Mustafar.

JEDI STARFIGHTER

GEONOSIAN STARFIGHTER

START →

1

5 ← 4 ← You run out of fuel. Miss a turn. ← 2 ←

15 → You receive orders to turn back. Return to the start. → 17 → 18 →

19 You find a shortcut. Have another turn.

One of your engines fails. Go back two spaces. ← 22 ← 21 ← 20 ←

33 → 34 → You are ordered to fly a different starship. Swap counter positions with the player on your right. → 36 →

37

41 ← You land to restock your supplies. Go back one space. ← 39 ← 38 ←

Your navigational equipment is upgraded. Go forward two spaces. → 52 → 53 → 54 → FINISH

Holocron Datafile:
Anakin's

Anakin Skywalker built his blue-and-silver Podracer in secret, dreaming of competing in the Boonta Eve Classic. It is smaller and more sleek than other Podracers, and it won him his freedom and a future as a Jedi. It is a machine that Anakin will never forget. Read and learn about Anakin's Podracer, and then use the grid to draw your own version.

Fact File

Even though he was merely a slave belonging to Watto the junk-shop owner, Anakin always had a genius for engineering. When a pair of Radon-Ulzer 620C racing engines came into the shop, Watto

Podracer

Did You Know?
Anakin's Podracer has a small cockpit pulled by two high-powered engines. An energy binder locks these engines together, and cables connect the engines to the cockpit.

decided that they were too burned out to be of any use. However, Anakin was able to repair them and use them in the Podracer of his dreams.

Anakin developed a new fuel atomiser and distribution system that sent more fuel into the combustion chambers, increasing his Podracer's top speed. He capped each Radon-Ulzer with air scoops that gave him extra control when braking and cornering.

After the Boonta Eve Classic, Qui-Gon Jinn sold Anakin's Podracer to Sebulba, who Anakin had beaten in the race. He repainted it and used it to win the Vinta Harvest Classic on Malastare.

DREAM DECODER

Do you remember your dreams? Some Jedi develop the ability to see the future in their dreams. However, it takes great skill and wisdom to understand what those dream-messages mean. Check the list right to see if you can understand the messages that come to you while you are asleep.

DREAM MEANING

BATTLE Pent up guilt or worry.
STARSHIP You will overcome obstacles.
ALIENS You are finding it hard to adapt.
ANCHOR Security and safety.
BEST FRIEND The things you value about yourself.
CLOAK How you want others to see you.
DROIDS You are acting without thinking.
EARS You need to accept help and advice from others.
KOUHUN Bad news is coming.
PROBE DROID Something new is going to happen.
YODA Let go of the past.
HAIR Thoughts and ideas.
HOUSE Yourself.
MAP You are on the path to success.
PLANET EARTH You need to be more realistic.
PADMÉ AMIDALA Luck.
RAIN Forgiveness.
ANAKIN SKYWALKER Doubt, guilt or betrayal.
THE EMPEROR A crisis in your life.
MACE WINDU Understanding and wisdom.
SPIDER DROID You're heading for danger.
TEETH Lies or careless talk.
JETPACK You need a change.
WARRIOR Your ability to cope with challenges.

Spot the Difference

There are ten differences between these pictures of Han flying his famous starship.
How many of them can you discover?

Revenge of the Sith

The Clone Wars had been raging for three years when droid leader General Grievous kidnapped Chancellor Palpatine. Obi-Wan and Anakin were sent to rescue him.

The Jedi drew on all their flying skills, dodging laser fire and droid fighters to reach General Grievous's ship the *Invisible Hand*. They battled their way on board and found Palpatine tied to a chair. At that moment, Count Dooku entered the room and engaged them both in a duel.

Obi-Wan was defeated and knocked out. While he was unconscious, Anakin disarmed Count Dooku and cut off his hands. He should have arrested him, but he was excited by his victory and Palpatine was urging him to kill the ex-Jedi. Anakin went against the Jedi code and cut off Count Dooku's head. General Grievous escaped, but Dooku was no more. It looked as if the end of the Clone Wars was close.

When he was safely back on Coruscant, Anakin

found out that his wife Padmé was pregnant. At first he was happy, but then he started to have nightmares that Padmé would die in childbirth. He was terrified of losing her. Just as the Jedi Council had seen when he was a child, he was full of fear.

The Jedi were beginning to feel suspicious of the Chancellor, but Anakin trusted him and believed in him. Knowing this, Palpatine made Anakin his representative on the Jedi Council. He wanted Anakin to spy for him, and Anakin saw it as a great honour. He thought that the Jedi Masters were unfair to the Chancellor. Palpatine told Anakin that the Sith had discovered how to stop death. Thinking of his nightmares, Anakin was eager to hear more. While Obi-Wan was busy finding and killing General Grievous, Anakin learned that Palpatine was really Darth Sidious, a Sith Lord. He was horrified and told the Jedi Council what he had discovered.

Mace went to arrest the Chancellor and they battled fiercely. As they duelled, Anakin realised that if Palpatine died, he would lose all chance of saving Padmé. Palpatine was no match for Mace, but the Jedi had not realised how close Anakin had come to the dark side. He saw Palpatine as his chance to save Padmé, so he cut off Mace's hand to stop him from killing the Chancellor. »

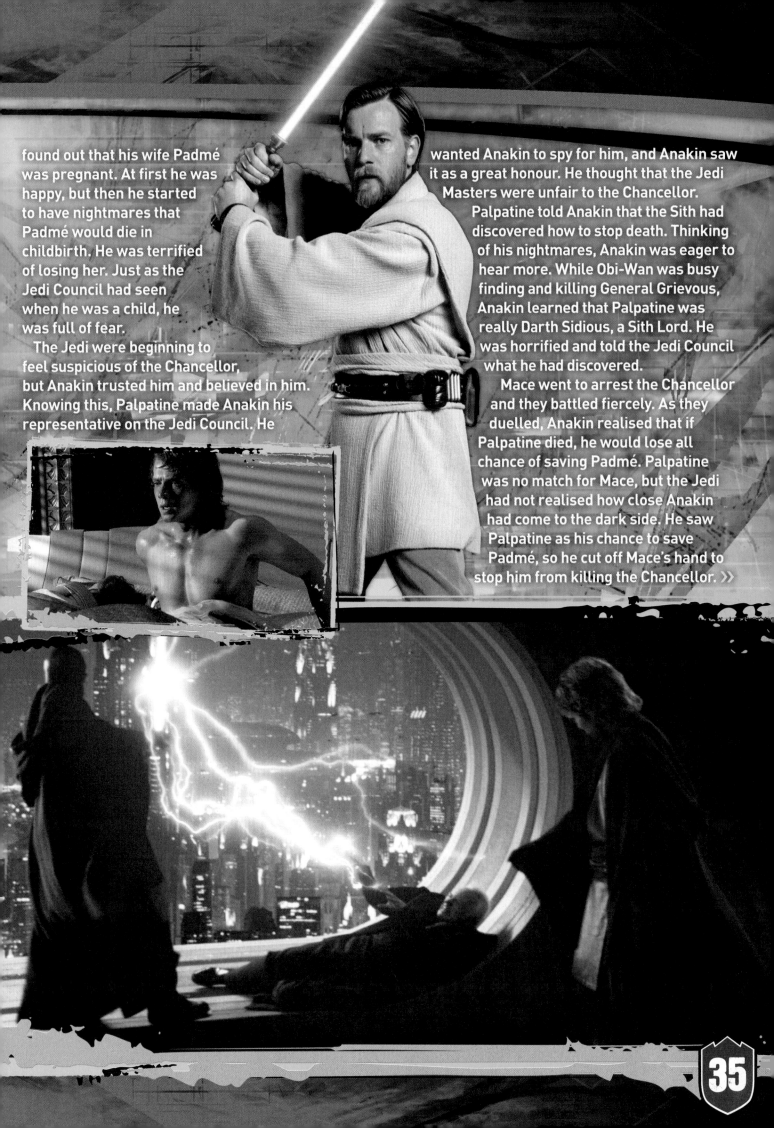

Revenge of the Sith

As Mace stared at Anakin in shock, Palpatine threw the Jedi Master to his death. Urged on by Palpatine, Anakin pledged himself to the ways of the Sith. From now on he would be known as Darth Vader.

The Jedi were declared enemies of the Republic, and Palpatine sent Anakin to the Jedi Temple to destroy all the Jedi there. Finally the Chancellor gave Order 66: kill all Jedi. Across the galaxy, clone soldiers turned on their Jedi generals.

Anakin went to Mustafar to kill the Separatists. He cut them down without mercy, his eyes glowing yellow with anger and bloodlust. Yoda and Obi-Wan realised that Anakin had turned to the dark side. The boy they had trained was gone forever – and Darth Vader had to be destroyed.

Palpatine announced that the Republic would be reorganised into the first Galactic Empire, ruled by him for life. Padmé was devastated, but she still believed in her husband's goodness. She knew that Anakin was on Mustafar and went to find him. She didn't know that Obi-Wan had stowed away aboard her ship.

When Anakin saw Obi-Wan, he thought that Padmé had betrayed him. He grabbed her by the throat and choked her, only letting her go to fight Obi-Wan. It was a fearsome duel, and it broke Obi-Wan's heart. But at last he cut Anakin down and left him to die.

On Coruscant, Master Yoda went to duel the Chancellor. The future of the galaxy depended on his success. But the Sith lord had incredible fighting skills, and eventually Yoda was defeated. Palpatine had won!

Padmé gave birth to a boy called Luke and a girl called Leia. She smiled at them, and then she

died. Anakin's betrayal had destroyed her. Meanwhile, Palpatine arrived on Mustafar to save Anakin. His twisted body was enclosed in hard black armour. He learned that he had killed Padmé, and his agony filled him with hatred, rage and despair.

As Yoda escaped to the planet Dagobah, Bail Organa took baby Leia to his wife. Meanwhile, Obi-Wan took Luke Skywalker to his uncle's farm on Tatooine. These children were now democracy's only hope for the future. ■

Holocron Datafile:
Solar Sailer

Count Dooku's ship was a gift from his Geonosian colleagues. It is a unique vessel, made from a melding of a *Punworcca* 116-class sloop with an elegant sail that the Count supplied himself. The sail provides independent power without the need to carry fuel. Read and learn about Count Dooku's vessel of choice, and then use the grid to draw a picture of the starship.

Did You Know?

Count Dooku used this ship to flee to Coruscant from Geonosis at the start of the Clone Wars.

Fact File

38

Geonosian Ship Design

The Geonosians have a long history of sailing. Long ago, they built cargo kites that could fly in their world's dense air. When they first ventured into space, they designed enormous, super-thin robotic sheets that worked on solar power. Later, they created heavier craft pushed from home by intense laser beams.

Did You Know?

An antiques dealer near the Gree Enclave sold the ancient sail to Count Dooku. It is powered by supralight emissions, giving Dooku's customised ship a style all its own.

SUMMARY

Homeworld: Geonosis
Weapon: 84 narrow tractor/repulsor beams
Affiliation: Confederacy of Independent Systems
Type: *Punworccca*-116-class interstellar sloop
Manufacturer: Huppla Pasa Tisc Shipwrights Collective
Maximum acceleration: Sail approximately 1,000G; thrusters 30G
Maximum airspeed: 992 mph
Crew: 1 droid pilot; optional living co-pilot
Passengers: 1 in cabin; standing room for 10
Hyperdrive: Class 1.5

The solar sailer uses unique technology to move through both realspace and hyperspace. It is shaped like a seed and has a bubble-like cockpit that contains the ship's droid pilot. When the body of the starship opens, the sail unfurls and gathers energetic particles for propulsion.

Like other Geonosian ships, the solar sailer uses an array of narrow tractor/repulsor beams. These act as offensive grapples and steering aids when there are objects around to push and pull against. This makes the vessel incredibly easy to manoeuvere.

In addition, the ray-shield energies can be adjusted to give the ship extra manoeuverablity.

HOW TO DRAW A REPUBLIC CRUISER

STEP 1

Draw a 3D box with a light pencil line.

The Republic cruiser was designed to be instantly recognisable by anyone in the galaxy. Its red colour scheme shows that it has diplomatic immunity. It might be on a mission for the Senate, the Supreme Chancellor or even the Jedi order. Follow these simple steps and learn how to draw this iconic starship.

STEP 2

Add these lines, pressing your pencil more heavily to create a darker line.

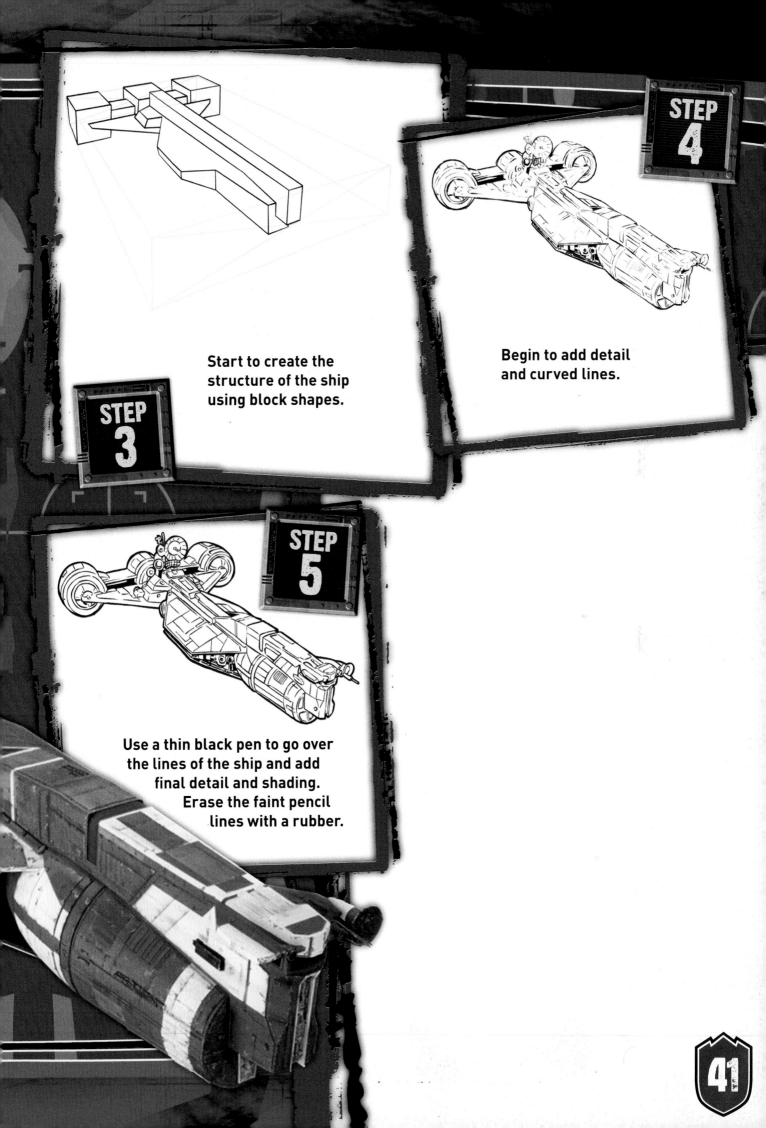

STEP 3

Start to create the
structure of the ship
using block shapes.

STEP 4

Begin to add detail
and curved lines.

STEP 5

Use a thin black pen to go over
the lines of the ship and add
final detail and shading.
Erase the faint pencil
lines with a rubber.

41

Wordsearch

There are twenty words connected with starships and technology hidden in this grid. Can you find them all?

```
R E O T F D B U H B M E O K M Y C I B A
E F O L T H S N M H W D L F S R R I N Z
T B E F Y S N D C A N N O N G O U I H V
H L M G B E E G S T A U L D E R I T W R
G M H E I V N D E L V U M T E M S N I S
I W W T J I Z E N G I N E O G P E R B M
F Y O K M R C Q W Y G D H P M T R L A H
T T U M O D I F I C A T I O N S Y O T P
B X R P R R J I U M T R J K N G T N T O
H C N Q J E E W H Y I U I G D N N W L T
U O D A D P Z G O N O J N F C I B H E J
L F H U L Y I R H Q N Q G B A W S R S A
L A U N C H M L C S U Y L O E T W O H E
G U H E Y T B M O E E I O A A K R E I Y
J J O I L E D N P T B U P T S F T T P N
V M E J L L T L A E T O W R W E K D Y V
B S H A O O A G T M N I O S T H R S L H
W X M E X C I V Y S R R B P U O L R P J
A I Q R C R S N T F R E P A I B P O O I
E D S A F V Z M S H I E L D L E V Z A O
```

Battleship ⬤	Fighter ⬤	Laser ⬤	Shield ⬤
Cannon ⬤	Frigate ⬤	Launch ⬤	TIE ⬤
Cruiser ⬤	Fuel ⬤	Modifications ⬤	Torpedo ⬤
Droid ⬤	Hull ⬤	Navigation ⬤	Weapons ⬤
Engine ⬤	Hyperdrive ⬤	Pilot ⬤	Wings ⬤

STARSHIP ENGINEER

A starship must meet the needs of the crew who will use it, and must also fulfil its prime purpose. Use these blueprints to plan the internal layout of a starship. As well as your own deck plans, you may want to include:

Airlocks
Bridge
Captain's Quarters
Cargo Hold
Cockpit
Computer Power
Substation
Conference Rooms
Crew Quarters
Decks
Dining Rooms
Docking Platform
Droid Maintenance
Room
Engine Room
Escape Pods
Library
Main Computer Room
Main Sensor Room
Officers' Common
Room
Officers' Quarters
Senor Power
Substation
State Room
Tech Station

Holocron Datafile:
AT-AT Walker

The All Terrain Armoured Transport is also known as the AT-AT walker. It is a four-legged transport and combat vehicle that can walk along the ground, and its appearance terrifies enemies of the Empire. Read and learn about the walker, and then use the grid to draw your own version of this formidable transport.

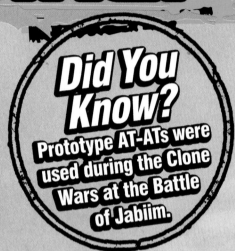

Did You Know?

Prototype AT-ATs were used during the Clone Wars at the Battle of Jabiim.

SUMMARY

Crew: 3
Passengers: 40
Cargo: 5 speeder bikes
Weapons:
2 heavy laser cannons,
2 medium blasters
Size: 15.5 m tall
20.6 m long
Affiliation: Empire

Fact File

The AT-AT walker is a vehicle used by the Empire for ground assaults. It was designed to move troops into occupied areas and terrify enemy forces. It has a heavy armour casing, which makes it very difficult to damage with any standard weapons.

Modifications

AT-ATs can be modified to suit different climates. For hot environments some weapons systems are replaced with Sienar z23 heat dissipation units to create dune walkers. Snow walkers feature added insulation, while the AT-AT swimmer uses repulsorlift units instead of legs.

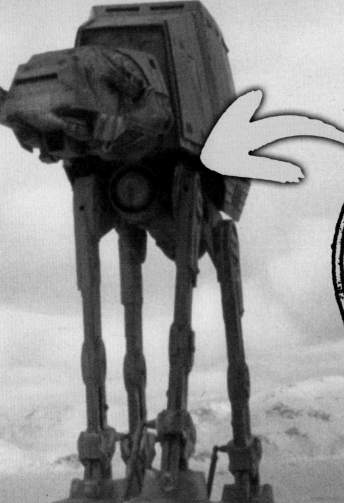

Did You Know?

The various components of the AT-ATs are made by a number of companies. However, the vehicles are put together at secret factories.

An AT-AT's head sits on top of a flexible neck and carries the main weapons, as well as the command crew. The crew consists of a commander, a gunner, and a pilot.

The walkers were designed to be unstoppable troop transports, but they work well as combat vehicles. Their four head-mounted laser cannons and heavy feet can reduce their enemies to dust. They can stride across a flat surface at high speed, and can also provide cover fire for ground troops. Because an AT-AT's head can move from side to side as well as up and down, it has a wide range of fire.

During a conflict, AT-ATs are lowered to a planet's surface on huge landing barges. As soon as they are in range of a target, they kneel and lower rear assault ramps. This allows the troops to embark.

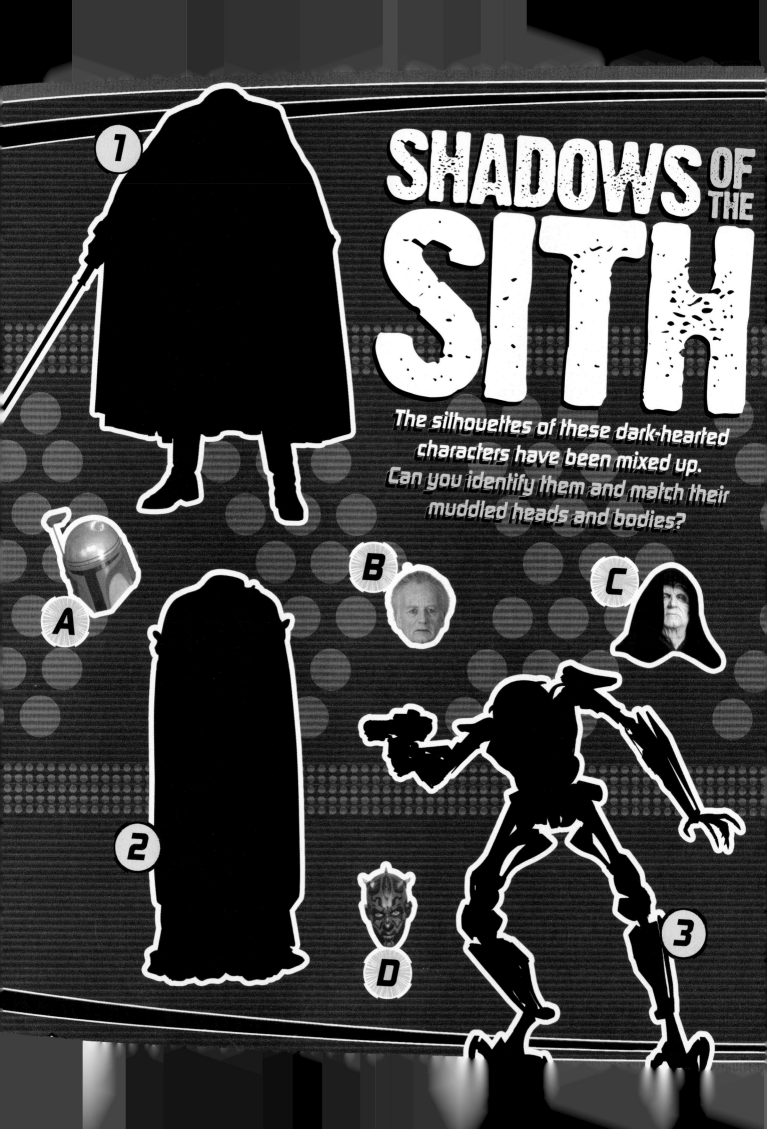

SHADOWS OF THE SITH

The silhouettes of these dark-hearted characters have been mixed up. Can you identify them and match their muddled heads and bodies?

A New Hope

Nineteen years had passed since the Galactic Republic had crumbled. The Rebel Alliance was doing all it could to fight against the evil Galactic Empire, and they were beginning to be troublesome to the Empire. Darth Vader was keen to stop them once and for all.

Rebel spies had managed to steal secret plans to the Empire's ultimate weapon, the Death Star. It was an armoured space station capable of destroying planets. Princess Leia of Alderaan was carrying the stolen plans aboard her starship.

Darth Vader caught up with the Princess's starship, but she had just enough time to give the plans to R2-D2, who escaped with C-3P0. They landed on the nearby planet of Tatooine, and after being captured by some scavenging Jawas they were bought by Owen Lars.

While Owen's nephew Luke was cleaning R2-D2, he dislodged part of a hidden message from Princess Leia. She had recorded it just before she was captured, begging Obi-Wan Kenobi for help.

Luke longed to hear the whole message, but R2-D2 blocked all his attempts. Frustrated, he went to have his dinner. While he was away, R2-D2 escaped and set off to find Obi-Wan.

Next morning, Luke took C-3PO to find the missing astromech droid. They found him with Obi-Wan Kenobi, who told Luke some of the truth about his past. He revealed that Luke's father had been a Jedi Knight and a gifted pilot. Obi-Wan gave Luke his father's lightsaber and told him about the Force.

When Obi-Wan heard the message from the Princess, he knew that he had to travel to Alderaan at once. He asked Luke to go with him, but Luke refused. He felt that he had to stay with his uncle.

When they returned to the Lars farm, everything changed. Darth Vader had sent his clone troopers to search for the droids, and they had murdered Luke's aunt and uncle. Luke was now alone, so he decided to join Obi-Wan on his mission to Alderaan.

At Mos Eisley spaceport, Obi-Wan hired a pilot called Han Solo to take them to Alderaan. He had a fast ship called the *Millennium Falcon*. Together with his Wookiee first mate, Chewbacca, Han owed money to the gangster Jabba the Hutt. They were eager to get away before Jabba had them killed.

In the meantime, the Death Star had reached Alderaan with Princess Leia aboard. Grand Moff Tarkin taunted her, before using his new weapon to destroy her home planet. »

A New Hope

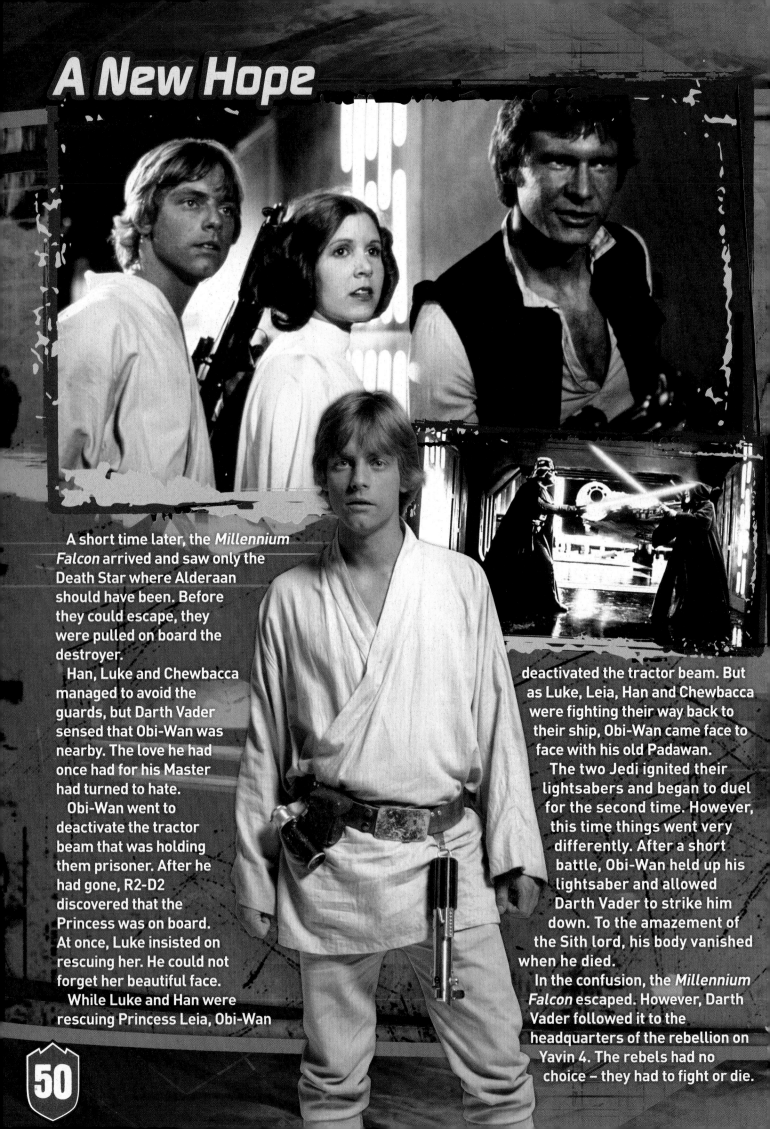

A short time later, the *Millennium Falcon* arrived and saw only the Death Star where Alderaan should have been. Before they could escape, they were pulled on board the destroyer.

Han, Luke and Chewbacca managed to avoid the guards, but Darth Vader sensed that Obi-Wan was nearby. The love he had once had for his Master had turned to hate.

Obi-Wan went to deactivate the tractor beam that was holding them prisoner. After he had gone, R2-D2 discovered that the Princess was on board. At once, Luke insisted on rescuing her. He could not forget her beautiful face.

While Luke and Han were rescuing Princess Leia, Obi-Wan

deactivated the tractor beam. But as Luke, Leia, Han and Chewbacca were fighting their way back to their ship, Obi-Wan came face to face with his old Padawan.

The two Jedi ignited their lightsabers and began to duel for the second time. However, this time things went very differently. After a short battle, Obi-Wan held up his lightsaber and allowed Darth Vader to strike him down. To the amazement of the Sith lord, his body vanished when he died.

In the confusion, the *Millennium Falcon* escaped. However, Darth Vader followed it to the headquarters of the rebellion on Yavin 4. The rebels had no choice – they had to fight or die.

The precious plans of the Death Star helped the Rebels to identify a weakness. If a pilot could fire one shot on a small thermal exhaust port, the entire battle station could be destroyed. However, the target area was only two metres wide. It would take an extraordinary pilot to make the shot.

Luke had always dreamed of being a pilot, so he decided to join the Rebel pilots and help. They were facing a terrifying enemy. Darth Vader was piloting his personal TIE fighter, and he was still one of the best pilots the galaxy had ever known.

When Luke flew towards the target, he aimed using the Force rather than his guidance computer. Darth Vader had stopped every fighter who tried to reach the thermal port so far, but he sensed that the Force was incredibly strong with Luke.

Darth Vader was close behind Luke when the *Millennium Falcon* appeared above him. Han blasted the Sith lord's fighter, sending it out of control. Thanks to him, Luke was able to send his photon torpedoes straight into the target, and the Death Star exploded.

There was still a long fight ahead. But for the first time in nearly twenty years, there was hope for the galaxy. ■

Crossword

Solve these tricky clues and complete the crossword.

Across

1 Which race scavenges for technology on Tatooine?

5 Who designed and built C-3PO?

6 A propulsion system that allows a starship to travel faster than light.

7 The lightsaber colour preferred by the Sith.

8 The AT-AT modification designed for hot climates.

9 The company that designed the X-wing starfighter.

11 Which planet did the Emperor's Death Star destroy?

Down

2 What is Chewbacca's species?

3 The weapon of a clone trooper.

4 _____ focus the energy from the power source in a lightsaber.

10 Who carries a purple lightsaber?

NEW YEAR: NEW JEDI

A true Jedi is always striving to become better. What will your resolutions be for 2012? Write them down here and check back in twelve months to see if you have kept them!

Holocron Datafile:
Millennium Falcon

This incredible vessel is known throughout the galaxy for the heroic part it played in the downfall of the Empire. With Han Solo and Chewbacca at the helm, it helped to defeat the Emperor and restore balance to the Force. Read and learn about the *Millennium Falcon*, and then use the grid to draw your own version of this famous ship.

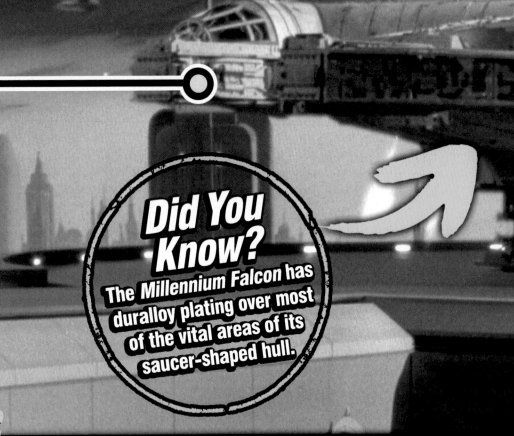

SUMMARY

Type: YT-1300 freighter
Manufacturer: Corellian Engineering Corporation
Size: 26.7 m long, 20 m wide, 5 m tall
Weapons: 2 quad laser cannons, 2 concussion missile tubes, blaster cannon
Engine: Class 0.5 hyperdrive
Top speed: 1,050 kph
Crew: 2 minimum
Passengers: 6
Cargo: 100 metric tons
Affiliation: Smuggling, Rebel Alliance

Did You Know?

The *Millennium Falcon* has duralloy plating over most of the vital areas of its saucer-shaped hull.

Fact File

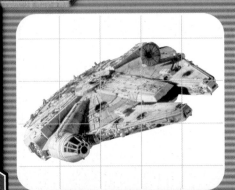

The *Millennium Falcon* proves that appearances can be deceptive. It looks as if it belongs in a junkyard, but in fact it is one of the fastest, best-equipped crafts in the galaxy. Constant (and illegal) modifications have turned

Ship's Owners

The ship was originally a YT-1300f, but an unlucky asteroid collision left the ship in an orbital junkyard near Nar Shaddaa. There, a technician used parts from a YT-1300p to restore the ship. It was then that the ship was named *Millennium Falcon*.

Following this, the ship was stolen by a pirate and then had several unscrupulous owners until it fell into the hands of a gambler called Lando Calrissian, who eventually lost it in a sabacc game to Han Solo.

Did You Know?
The ship's two AG-2G cannons draw directly from the *Falcon's* Quadex power core.

the *Falcon* into a completely unique vessel. Its ramshackle appearance has helped it to escape many Imperial officers and Customs officials. But inside, it has some powerful secrets.

The ship contains a hyperdrive that is nearly twice as fast as any Imperial warship's, a first-class sensor-suite array, shielded smuggling compartments, an Imperial deflector shield system, two quad laser cannons, two concussion missile launchers and a retractable light laser cannon.

However, these modifications have made the *Millennium Falcon* unpredictable and its reconditioned hyperdrive often fails — usually at the worst possible moments.

Technology

A

B

1 Name the Ship

Can you identify which ship each of these photos shows?

B

C

D

Answer these questions and test your understanding of galactic technology.

B

A

C

2 Name the Warrior

Who are the owners of these weapons?

D

Test

3 A.K.A.

Each of these people is known by more than one name. Can you remember the alias of each one?

A

B

C

D

4 In Service

These characters began their lives in service. But which organisations did they serve?

A

B

C

D

Check your answers and award yourself one point for every correct answer.

1–6
Return to your studies. You have a lot more to learn!

7–11
You have done well, but there is still room for improvement. Work on developing your memory skills.

12–16
Your knowledge and understanding is excellent – there may be a future for you in technology development.

FILL IN THE GAPS

Some important words are missing from these sentences. Can you put all the words in the right places?

1 _____ _____ _____ are huge, circular vessels with a central _____ structure.

2 Blasters fire beams of intense _____ _____. They have settings ranging from stun to _____.

3 Darth Vader's _____ connects with a flat backpack to cycle air in and out of his lungs. It also helps to keep his damaged _____ in shape.

4 The Kaminoans produce a variety of _____ and other high-tech weapons and _____ for their clients.

5 _____ ____ come in all shapes and sizes. They range from small capsules that can hold only one passenger to enormous _____ that can hold over a dozen passengers.

6 Each battle droid has an _____ _____ printed on its ____.

7 Droidekas are heavily armed droids that can transform into large, metal _____. They are also known as _____ droids. They have twin laser _____ and are protected by personal deflector shields.

8 Jabba the Hutt uses his _____ _____ ____ for personal business trips. It can reach speeds of up to 800 kph when it is in the _____.

ATMOSPHERE	IDENTIFICATION NUMBER	SKULL
BACK	LIFEBOATS	SPHERICAL
CANNONS	LIGHT ENERGY	TRADE FEDERATION
DESTROYER	LUXURY YACHT SHIP	BATTLESHIPS
ESCAPE PODS	MISSILES	VAPORISE
HELMET	SABERDARTS	WHEELS

ANAGRAMS

CAN YOU FIGURE OUT THE OFFICIAL TITLES THAT ARE HIDDEN IN THESE ANAGRAMS?

1 CLEAN CAPTION

2 ROPER ME

3 STREAM

4 AND A PAW

5 MODERN MAC

6 MAD LAIR

7 DROL

8 TREASON

Holocron Datafile:
Death Star

The Death Star is an enormous battle station that strikes terror into the hearts of the Empire's enemies. It is the largest starship ever built and has a superlaser that has been designed to destroy planets. Read and learn about the Death Star, and then use the grid to draw your own version of this ultimate weapon.

ON BOARD THE DEATH STAR

4 capital ships
1,860 drop-ships
2,840 blastboats
3,600 assault shuttles
7,200 TIE fighters
11,016 land vehicles
13,000 support craft

Did You Know?
The Death Star can withstand a full assault by huge enemy starships.

Plots and Plans

The Geonosians had the plans for the Death Star during the Battle of Geonosis. They gave the schematics to Count Dooku to pass to his master, Darth Sidious.

Did You Know?

The Death Star was constructed in hidden orbital construction deep in the Outer Rim.

Fact File

The Death Star is the size of a small moon, and can carry over a million individuals. It is armed with thousands of turbolasers and ion cannons, as well as vast numbers of TIE fighters and other ships. It is the invention of Grand Moff Tarkin, whose cruelty is legendary.

The battle station is intended to crush the Rebellion once and for all. It can reduce entire planets to dust, and is quickly spreading fear throughout the galaxy. Even before it became fully operational, its prisons were filling up. Many political troublemakers, Rebels, pirates and enemies of the Empire have entered the battle station, never to be seen again.

Although it is a terrible weapon, the Death Star does have one weakness. An insignificant exhaust port leads straight into the main reactor. However, it is such a tiny target that the Imperial officers are sure that it cannot be a problem.

The Empire Strikes Back

Three years after the Battle of Yavin, things were not going well for the Rebel Alliance. They had been driven from their hidden base and chased across the galaxy by Imperial forces. Their current secret base was on the remote ice world of Hoth.

Darth Vader had sent probes across the galaxy to search for the Rebels, and Luke saw one of them as he was finishing a routine patrol. He went to investigate, but a wampa attacked him and dragged him away to its cave.

When the Rebels realised that Luke was missing, they knew his life was in danger. The snowy wastes of Hoth were deadly at night. Han Solo set out to search, willing to risk his life for his friend.

Meanwhile, Luke used his lightsaber to free himself and escape from the cave. Due to his injuries and the freezing cold, he collapsed in the snow. He had a vision of Obi-Wan Kenobi, who told him to go to the Dagobah system and learn from Yoda. Luke passed out, but luckily Han found him and saved his friend's life.

Darth Vader's probe had done its job, and he was on his way to Hoth. The Rebels' sensors warned them, and they prepared to evacuate the base.

When Darth Vader arrived, some Rebels were still on the base. The Sith Lord ordered a surface attack and a vicious battle began. Luke fought alongside his fellow Rebels and risked his life to destroy their walkers. Finally the evacuation was complete,

and Luke set a course for the Dagobah system with R2-D2.

The Emperor told Darth Vader that Luke was his son. He also said that Luke must not become a Jedi, because the Force was so strong with him that he could destroy them all. The Emperor wanted to turn him to the dark side, just as he had turned Anakin Skywalker.

Han, Chewbacca, Princess Leia and C-3PO were aboard the *Millennium Falcon*, which had a damaged hyperdrive. They set a course for a nearby mining colony, which was run by Lando Calrissian. There they would find the parts they needed to repair their hyperdrive. However, they were followed by a bounty hunter – the infamous Boba Fett.

On Dagobah, Luke met Yoda for the first time. At first he found it hard to believe that this small green creature was a Jedi Master, but eventually he accepted Yoda's wisdom. »

Leia did not trust him. She was right to be suspicious. Lando betrayed them all to Darth Vader because it was the only way he could save his people. Han was frozen solid in carbonite and sent to Jabba the Hutt.

Luke was improving, but his training was interrupted when he had a vision of his friends in danger. He was determined to go and rescue them without finishing his training. Yoda could not change his mind.

Darth Vader knew Luke would come to rescue his friends. When the young man arrived at the mining colony, he found himself facing the terrifying Sith Lord. They ignited their lightsabers and began to fight.

Meanwhile, Lando was feeling very guilty about betraying his friend. He was supposed to keep Princess Leia, C-3PO and Chewbacca prisoner, but decided to set them free. Together, they found R2-D2 and flew away in the *Millennium Falcon.*

Luke fought well, but Darth Vader was more experienced and more

Luke worked hard, and his training was tough. Yoda passed on the wisdom of the Jedi Order, hoping that Luke could overcome his fear and doubts. In the past, a Jedi was trained from childhood. Could Luke learn everything he needed to know in time to save the galaxy?

When the *Millennium Falcon* landed at the mining colony it was met by Lando. He was an old friend of Han, but Princess

skilful. At last, Luke fell onto a platform above an abyss and was at the Sith Lord's mercy. Darth Vader cut off his right hand, and Luke prepared to die. But to his astonishment, Darth Vader revealed that he was Luke's father.

Luke was in a state of shock. Darth Vader began to tell him that it was his destiny to turn to the dark side. He encouraged Luke to help him destroy the Emperor, saying that they could rule the galaxy together as father and son. But Luke would rather die than betray his friends and turn to the dark side. He rolled himself over the edge of the platform and dropped into the abyss.

He fell onto a metal frame below the city and managed to cling on, not knowing how he could possibly escape. In his despair, he called out for Leia. And somehow, on the far-away *Millennium Falcon*, Leia heard him. She insisted they turn around. Luke needed her.

Through his connection with the Force, Darth Vader sensed that Luke was still alive. He tried to stop the *Millennium Falcon*, but it went into hyperspace and escaped. For now, Anakin Skywalker's son was safe. ◼

NEW JEDI KNIGHT

If you were a Jedi Master, how would you train your Padawan? What do you think makes the ideal Jedi Knight? Use these questions to create the perfect Jedi. Then draw a picture of your creation and write his or her name on the right.

name:

JEDI MASTER:

STRENGTHS:

WEAKNESSES:

HOME PLANET:

WHERE WAS HE/SHE DISCOVERED?:

WHICH JEDI DISCOVERED HIM/HER?:

BEST SKILLS:

FIGHTING STYLE:

FIRST MISSION:

LIGHTSABER COLOUR:

TRANSPORT:

MOST SIGNIFICANT LIGHTSABER DUEL:

GREATEST MOMENT:

MOST EMBARRASSING MOMENT:

CLOSEST FRIEND:

Holocron Datafile:
Darth Vader's TIE

One of Darth Vader's favourite possessions is his prototype starfighter, which is easily recognisable due to its distinctive bent wings. It has a deflector shield generator, a small hyperdrive system and fixed twin heavy-blaster cannons, but no life support systems. Read and learn about the TIE Advanced, and then use the grid to draw your own version of this superb craft.

Fact File

The TIE Advanced has a durasteel-alloy hull, elongated rear deck and solar array wings, as well as shield generators and heavy armour plating. It has P-s5.6 twin ion engines, but its I-S3a solar ionisation reactor is more powerful than those on the standard TIE.

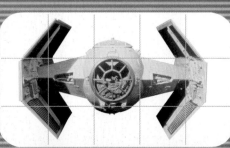

The TIE Advanced is incredibly effective in battle because it can take many direct hits without being destroyed. The hyperdrive system allows it to flee hopeless battles.

The Empire decided not to order large numbers of the TIE Advanced x1, saying that they cost too much. The designer, Sienar, incorporated the ship's best qualities into the design of the new TIE interceptor.

Advanced Fighter

Battle of Yavin

Darth Vader used the fighter at the Battle of Yavin, where it was clipped by the *Falcon's* quad laser cannons. It spun off into space, but Vader eventually regained control and fled to the Imperial outpost at Vaal.

The TIE Advanced was repaired and stayed in Vader's possession. It was finally destroyed at the Battle of Endor when the Super Star Destroyer crashed into the second Death Star.

SUMMARY

Top Speed: 1,200 kph
Cannon Fire Colour:
Green
Length: 9.2 metres
Crew: 1
Passengers: none
Weapons:
2 laser cannons

Did You Know?
Wampas may look mindless, but they are capable of being very cunning.

WAMPA

Wampas are wild carnivores that roam the wastelands of Hoth. Their shaggy white fur is usually stained by blood and gore, and their yellow teeth and sharp claws are designed for slaughter. Their curved horns grow as they age.

They cover vast amounts of terrain searching for food, and have evolved to be magnificent hunters. They have a very faint scent, which stops their prey from detecting them. They also never hunt when they are hungry, and they fiercely guard their hunting grounds. A wampa will stun its victims and then drag them to its lair. There, it will eat them at its leisure.

Did You Know?
Wampas do not show up on most life-form sensors.

MONSTERS OF THE GALAXY

SARLACC

A sarlacc is an ugly, many-tentacled creature. Its mouth is coated in mucus and lined by rows of teeth, but that is only a fraction of the size of the overall creature. It uses its powerful tentacles to drag prey into its gullet, where legend says it takes 1,000 years to be digested.

One of the most infamous sarlaccs lives in the Great Pit of Carkoon of Tatooine. Jabba the Hutt enjoys feeding his enemies into its jaws. The Pit of Carkoon's sandy slopes send the prey sliding into the Sarlacc's mouth.

Did You Know?
Sarlaccs start life as small organisms flying through space. When they find a suitable planet, they land and begin to grow as spores.

Did You Know?
Jabba the Hutt tried to feed Luke Skywalker to the sarlacc in the Pit of Carkoon.

Did You Know?
Jabba the Hutt keeps an untamed rancor underneath his throne room.

RANCOR

Rancors are terrifying, bloodthirsty carnivores, bristling with claws and fangs. They stand over five metres tall and have an appetite for raw flesh. The size and strength of rancors is intimidating, and they are very difficult to kill. Their thick skin gives them good protection from weapon fire.

On Dathomir, the planet of the witches, rancors are domesticated as mounts and hunting animals. They are also found in the Ottethan system.

Rancors reproduce by laying eggs and burying them in a warm area to incubate. Both male and female rancors guard the nest for three months until the eggs hatch.

Did You Know?
Count Dooku has boots made from rancor

71

Holocron Datafile:
74-Z Speeder

Speeder bikes are small personal transports used by Imperial scout troops for reconnaissance. They are much easier to manoeuvre than landspeeders or airspeeders, but they have minimal armour and one mistake by the pilot can result in a fatal crash. Read and learn about speeder bikes, and then use the grid to draw your own version of this simple transport.

Fact File

Speeder bikes are powered by very efficient engines, and they are used as recreational vehicles as well as simple transports. Because of their speed, ease of use and low cost, they are the perfect reconnaissance craft.

Speeders can rise about 25 metres above the ground. This helps them to travel across all types of terrain, including dense forests, at extremely high speeds. The pilot steers the speeder bike by using the vehicle's handgrips. Speed and altitude are controlled through the foot pedals. Sensors, the targeting system and the firing mechanism are in front of the saddle.

Several military models have been manufactured for use by Imperial forces. Military speeder bikes have light armour plating and a single blaster cannon.

The clone army used speeder bikes during the Battle of Geonosis. They were donated by the Aratech Repulsor Company.

Bike

Did You Know?
Princess Leia and Luke Skywalker used stolen speeder bikes to chase stormtroopers on Endor during a vital mission for the Rebel Alliance.

Did You Know?
The Empire deploys speeders in groups of four, which are collectively called 'lances'.

SUMMARY

Size: 4.4 m long
Top Speed: 500kph
Manufacturer: Aratech Repulsor Company
Weapons:
Light blaster cannon
Pilot: 1
Passengers: 1
Cargo capacity: 3 to 4 kg

Return of the Jedi

Han Solo, frozen in carbonite, had been taken to the palace of Jabba the Hutt. The gangster found it amusing to hang the frozen smuggler on his wall, as a warning to anyone else who defied him. But Han's friends got into the castle and managed to release Han from his carbonite prison. However, Jabba the Hutt captured them before they could escape. He condemned Luke and Han to a lingering death in the Pit of Carkoon.

Jabba the Hutt had not realised how skilled Luke had become. The corrupt Hutt was killed, and Boba Fett was thrown into the pit instead.

The Galactic Empire was building a new Death Star, and when it was completed the Rebels would be wiped out. On the half-completed Death Star, Lord Vader met the Emperor. They agreed they had to turn Luke to the dark side together.

Luke returned to the Dagobah system to complete his training, but he found Yoda dying. Yoda said that Luke needed no more training, but that he had to face Darth Vader before he could be a true Jedi. When Yoda died he became one with

the Force and his body vanished. As Luke grieved, he had another vision of Obi-Wan.

Obi-Wan said that the dark side of the Force had seduced his old Padawan, and that Anakin no longer existed. But Luke could not believe that there was no goodness left in his father. He refused to agree to kill him.

Obi-Wan thought this meant the Emperor would win. He revealed that Princess Leia was Luke's twin sister, but Luke would not change his mind.

Luke rejoined the Rebels, who were making plans to destroy the half-completed Death Star. They had decided to deactivate its energy shield, which was powered from the forest moon of Endor. As soon as the shield was down, their fighters could destroy the ultimate weapon. Han was going to lead the strike team to Endor with Luke, Leia and Chewbacca. It was Lando's job to lead the attack on the Death Star.

As soon as Han's strike team arrived on Endor, Darth Vader sensed Luke's presence. The Emperor knew Luke would seek his father out. He told Darth Vader to go to Endor and wait for his son.

The strike team met a tribe of Ewoks who lived on Endor. While they were in the Ewoks' treetop home, Luke told Leia the truths that he had learned. As she tried to take it all in, Luke said he was going to leave the strike team. He knew that Darth Vader could sense his presence, and he felt that he was putting his friends in danger. »

Return of the Jedi

Luke gave in to his destiny. He surrendered to Darth Vader, and met his father face-to-face for the second time. He tried to reach Anakin Skywalker, asking him to let go of his hatred. Darth Vader doubted himself for the first time in years. But the Emperor's hold on him was deep and Luke could not break through.

Darth Vader took Luke to the Emperor on board the Death Star. There, the evil Emperor told him he knew about the Alliance attack – the Rebels were in a trap. As the Alliance fleet set off for Endor, the strike team was overpowered by clone troopers.

The Alliance fleet came out of hyperspace to find that the shield was still operational. They were attacked by Imperial fighters and a desperate battle began as Luke watched from the Death Star.

The Emperor played on every weakness that Luke possessed. He tried to force Luke to give in to his anger, and he could sense he was succeeding. Finally Luke's rage bubbled to the surface and he tried to strike the Emperor, but he was stopped by Darth Vader's lightsaber. Father and son duelled once more. It seemed as if the Emperor was going to succeed. But down on

Endor, the brave Ewoks attacked the clone troopers. As they battled, Han and Leia broke free and raced to deactivate the shield generator.

Luke was filled with anger, and he fought Darth Vader with every ounce of strength and skill he possessed. Finally, a furious swipe of his lightsaber cut off his father's right hand. The Emperor laughed in delight, but Luke was horrified. He vowed he would never turn to the dark side.

The Emperor flung Force lightning at Luke, throwing him to the ground in agony. As the shield generator was destroyed and Lando's team locked their weapons on to the Death Star, Darth Vader watched his son writhing on the floor.

Seeing Luke at the mercy of the Emperor finally made Anakin Skywalker cast off the evil that had possessed him for so long. He picked up the Emperor and threw him down the power shaft, the Force lightning crackling around him.

As his Master died, Anakin Skywalker collapsed to the floor and Luke held him in his arms. Anakin died in his son's arms. Then the Death Star began to explode from within, and Luke flew out on board a small fighter.

The murderous Empire had been destroyed, the galaxy was free, and the Jedi Order had returned at last. ■

answers

page 33

page 12

1. False 2. True 3. False
4. False 5. True 6. False
7. True 8. False 9. False 10. True

page 42

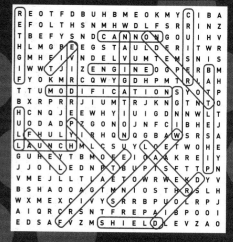

page 16

L I G H T S A B E R
S T A R F I G H T E R
U N D E R W A T E R
P O D
E L E C T R O S T A F F

pages 46-47

1. G 2. F 3. E 4. B 5. D 6. A
7. C 8. H

page 17

Odd One Out: D

page 52

page 26

pages 56-57

1. **Name the ship:**
a. The *Millennium Falcon*
b. The *Death Star*

page 27